Packed full of roar-some dinosaur fun!

Get ready to go back in time to when dinosaurs roamed the Earth...

This book belongs to

Abdullad

Write your name here.

Published 2020.

Little Brother Books Ltd, Ground Floor, 23 Southernhay East, Exeter, Devon, EX1 1QL

Printed In Poland.

books@littlebrotherbooks.co.uk | www.littlebrotherbooks.co.uk

The Little Brother Books trademark, email and website addresses, are the sole and exclusive properties of Little Brother Books Limited.

Terrific Tyrannosaurus

Meet one of the scariest dinosaurs to ever roam the Earth!

DINO FACTS

NAME: Tyrannosaurus
(tye-RAN-oh-sore-us)

MEANING: Tyrant lizard

SIZE:

FOOD: Meat

WOW!

TYRANNOSAURUS

Mighty Bite

The ferocious Tyrannosaurus had 60 thick, sharp teeth packed into its huge mouth. Its mighty jaws could crush any animal.

Little Arms

Although the Tyrannosaurus was HUGE, its arms were tiny compared to the rest of its body.

A Tyrannosaurus's bite could have dented cars if they'd been around at the same time.

Fierce Family

Tyrannosaurus lived in Canada and the USA but it had a cousin in Asia, named Tarbosaurus, that looked almost exactly the same.

Big Brain

Tyrannosaurus gets the prize for biggest brain – it was twice the size of other giant meat-eaters'. Does that mean it was twice as clever?

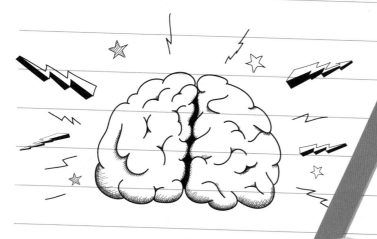

T-REX TEASER

Which shadow belongs to the Tyrannosaurus?

a

b

c

d

Answers on pages 76-77.

Prehistoric Search

Get your binoculars ready and go back in time to spot the small images in the big picture below.

Tick as you spot each one.

Armoured Ankylosaurus

This slow moving dino was pretty tough.

DINO FACTS

NAME: Ankylosaurus
(an-KIE-loh-sore-us)

MEANING: Stiff lizard

SIZE:

FOOD: 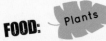 Plants

ANKYLOSAURUS

Fast Food

Instead of chewing its food, the Ankylosaurus swallowed it whole and it was broken down inside its stomach. That's one way to speed up mealtimes!

Tough Dino

Bulky Ankylosaurus was as big as a tank and its tough armour made it nearly as hard to attack.

Ankylosaurus had little leaf-shaped teeth that were perfect for snipping plants.

OUCH!

Deadly Defence

An Ankylosaurus tail was a deadly weapon. Made of seven bones joined together, it could break attackers' bones with a well-aimed swing.

QUESTION TIME

What did the Anklosaurus like to eat? Copy the letters below into the matching coloured circles to find out.

E S V E L

Dino Alert!

These little dinosaurs have just hatched. Can you match each baby dino to the egg it came out of?

Clue
The dinosaurs' eggs are the same colour as they are.

1

2

3

4

5

a

b

c

d

e

Answers on pages 76-77.

Colouring Fun

Grab your favourite pens and add some cool colours to this mighty dinosaur.

SPOT IT!

Can you find this flying reptile?

Colour the footprints when you've finished.

13

Vicious Velociraptor

This small dinosaur was fast on its feet.

DINO FACTS

NAME: Velociraptor
(vel-OSS-ee-rap-tor)

MEANING:
Speed thief

SIZE:

FOOD: Meat

BRAINY!

Smart Dino

For such a small dinosaur, the Velociraptor had a BIG brain. It would have been one of the smartest raptors at dino school!

Useful Tail

The Velociraptor was only the size of a poodle but it could move quickly. Its tail might have helped it keep its balance as it ran.

VELOCIRAPTOR

Tight Grip

Velociraptors had three claws on each hand which they used to grip onto their prey.

DID YOU KNOW?

Vicious Velociraptors lived in Mongolia 80 million years ago.

Finding Food

Meat-eating Velociraptors hunted in

packs and probably feasted on small lizards,

mammals and dinosaur eggs.

RHYME TIME

Velociraptors ate meat. Circle the words that rhyme with meat.

HEAT   GREET

FUN   FEET   LEAF

Answers on pages 76-77.

Exciting Expedition

Imagine you're going on an expedition to discover dinosaurs! Grab your explorer's hat and plan your adventure below.

Draw yourself underneath this explorer's hat.

Which dinosaur do you hope to see?

Triceratops

Ankylosaurus

Tyrannosaurus

Circle what you will take with you.

How do you feel?

EXCITED

BRAVE

NERVOUS

Circle where you are going on your expedition.

A volcano

The desert

The shoreline

What will you do after your expedition?

Write about what I saw.

Have a nice long sleep.

Eat dinner.

17

Performing Parasaurolophus

Find out all about the dinosaur that could make music.

QUACK!

PARASAUROLOPHUS

Quack Quack

Parasaurolophus was a duckbill dinosaur. It had a wide, flat mouth a bit like a duck's beak.

DINO FACTS

NAME: Parasaurolophus
(pa-ra-saw-ROL-off-us)

MEANING:
Near crested lizard

SIZE:

FOOD: Plants

Music Time

Parasaurolophus had a fancy crest on its head that made a sound like a trumpet. Who knew dinosaurs could make music!

Fossil Finds

Lots of skeleton and skull fossils have been found in the USA and Canada where Parasaurolophus lived.

DID YOU KNOW?

The sound from its crest might have been how the Parasaurolophus communicated with other dinosaurs.

Favourite Food

As vegetarians, Parasaurolophus enjoyed eating plants. They could stand on their back legs to reach leaves that were high up.

LOTS OF LEAVES

How many leaves can you count in this pile?

Write your answer here

Answers on pages 76-77.

19

Heading Home

Draw a path to lead this baby Brachiosaurus back to its mummy.
Don't forget to complete the activities along the way.

START

Don't step on the dinosaur eggs.

WHEEEE!
Slide down the Apatosaurus's tail!

Colour some leaves for the baby Brachiosaurus to eat.

Count the fossils.

Colour the footprints to lead the baby dinosaur to its mummy.

Mummy

FINISH

Answers on pages 76-77.

21

Huge Diplodocus

This gigantic creature had a really looooong neck and tail!

WOW!

Giant Dino

The enormous Diplodocus was one of the largest dinosaurs. It was as long as a blue whale but not that heavy for its size.

Easy Eating

The long, thin, pointy teeth of a Diplodocus were perfectly designed to strip leaves from trees. Just like a built in knife and fork!

Noisy Tail

A Diplodocus used its long tail like a whip. The loud booming sound it made when the giant dinosaur snapped it might have scared off predators. Cool!

High Head?

Scientists can't agree whether the long-necked Diplodocus would have been able to hold its head up high. It might have been too hard for its heart to pump blood that far upwards.

DID YOU KNOW?

The Diplodocus is the longest dinosaur for which a complete skeleton has been found.

DINO FACTS

NAME: Diplodocus
(DIP-low DOCK-us)

MEANING: Double beam

SIZE:

FOOD: Plants

FOSSIL FUN

Which of these fossils shows a Diplodocus?

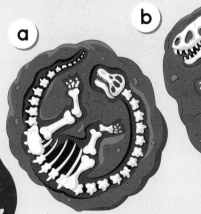
a

b

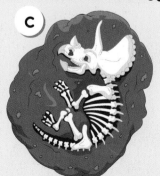
c

Answers on pages 76-77.

Dino Hat

Dress up as a dinosaur with this cool dino hat. It's super easy to make!

YOU WILL NEED

Thin card in green, red and yellow

White paper   Pencil

Stapler

Black felt tip pen

Ruler

Scissors   Glue

HOW TO MAKE

10cm

1 Cut out a strip of green card, 10cm wide, long enough to fit around your head. You may have to stick two strips together.

2 Staple the ends of the card strip together to make a band shape.

3 Cut a triangle out of red card and glue it on to the front of your band.

24

4 Cut two triangles out of yellow card and glue them either side of the red triangle.

5 Cut two small circles out of white paper and draw black circles on them to make eyes. Glue the eyes on to your band.

ROAR!

6 Use the black pen to draw two black dots for a nose. Put your hat on your head and roar like a dinosaur!

Follow the footprints to the Ankylosaurus then colour it in.

Adult guidance is needed for this activity.

25

Desert Oviraptor

Read on to find out more about this interesting meat-eater.

Toothless Dino

Although they didn't have any teeth, Oviraptors were meat-eating dinosaurs. They may have swallowed reptiles whole rather than chewing flesh.

DINO FACTS

NAME: Oviraptor
(OH-vee-RAP-tor)

MEANING: Egg thief

SIZE:

FOOD: Meat   Plants

The Wrong Name

Oviraptors were given the name 'egg thief' after an explorer mistakenly thought they stole eggs from other dinosaurs. Nearly 70 years later, this was proved to be untrue.

OVIRAPTOR

26

Desert Dino

Oviraptors were desert dinosaurs living in Mongolia and China. One fossil found showed an Oviraptor still on top of its nest after it had been buried in sand.

DID YOU KNOW?

Oviraptors laid their eggs in a spiral shape inside their nest.

Cosy Nest

Oviraptors may have had feathered wings which they used to shelter their babies in the nest. A bit like a warm blanket!

QUICK QUESTION

The Oviraptor had sharp teeth.
Circle the right answer.

TRUE   FALSE

Answers on pages 76-77.

Beat the Clock

See how quickly you can spot the eight dino differences between these two pictures?

HOW LONG DID IT TAKE?

Less than a minute = colour the clock red.

1-3 minutes = colour the clock blue.

More than 3 minutes = colour the clock green.

READY, STEADY, GO!

Colour a dinosaur footprint each time you spot a change.

1 2 3 4 5 6 7 8

Answers on pages 76-77.

Looooong Spinosaurus

Meet the dinosaur with the mysterious sail.

DINO FACTS

NAME: Spinosaurus
(SPINE-oh-SORE-us)

MEANING: Thorn lizard

SIZE:

FOOD: Meat   Fish

Long Length

Spinosaurus was the longest of all the meat-eating dinosaurs and may have grown up to a whopping 15m - that's nearly as long as two buses!

Water Home

Some scientists think that Spinosaurus lived in shallow waters. It had webbed toes which would have helped it walk along the bottom of rivers.

Hunting Style

Spinosaurus had long, narrow jaws, a bit like a crocodile's, and high up nostrils for breathing in the water. It probably caught fish to eat rather than hunting animals on land.

DID YOU KNOW?

As well as fish, Spinosaurus probably ate flying pterosaurs.

Super Sail

Spinosaurus had an impressive sail but no one really knows what it was for. It could have helped the dinosaur stay underwater or store up energy.

ODD ONE OUT

Which of these Spinosaurus pictures is the odd one out?

b

a

c

Answers on pages 76-77.

Match It

Watch out, there are dinosaurs about!
Can you match each dinosaur to its shadow?

How many dinosaur eggs are hidden on these pages?

Almighty Allosaurus

Lots of dinosaurs were in danger when this giant predator was about!

Dinosaur King

Allosaurus lived in the USA and Portugal 145 million years ago. In North America this gigantic dino was the king of the Jurassic predators.

DINO FACTS

NAME: Allosaurus
(AL-oh-saw-russ)

MEANING: Other lizard

SIZE:

FOOD: Meat

Mighty Mouthful

The fierce Allosaurus had 70 dagger-like teeth in its powerful jaws. They curved backwards so that its prey couldn't escape.

Dino Danger

Hundreds of Allosaurus bones have been found in one place in Utah, USA. Scientists think these built up over time so there might have been something dangerous in that area, such as a huge pit the Allosaurus could fall into.

DID YOU KNOW?

Allosaurus could bend its lower jawbones outwards to make room in its mouth for big chunks of meat.

Tight Grip

Allosaurus had three-fingered hands with very strong claws. It would have been hard to escape from its powerful grip.

POWERFUL!

DINO COLOURING

Colour this fearsome Allosaurus.

Who's Next?

These dinosaurs are making patterns. Can you work out which one is missing from the end of each row?

1  **?**

2 **?**

3 **?**

4 **?**

COUNT IT!

How many dinosaur footprints can you count?

Answers on pages 76-77.

Dino Dot-to-Dot

Join the dots to finish this dinosaur picture then add some roar-some colours.

SPOT IT!

Can you find this meteor in the sky?

37

Horned Triceratops

Read on to find out more about the dinosaur with the frill.

Lots of Teeth

Triceratops was a plant eater with 800 tiny teeth in its beak-like mouth. Imagine how long a visit to the dentist would have taken!

DINO FACTS

NAME: Triceratops
(tri-SERRA-tops)

MEANING:
Three-horned face

SIZE:

FOOD: Plants

Big Dino

The Triceratops was the biggest of the horned dinosaurs and the last one to walk the Earth. It lived in Canada and the USA 68 to 66 million years ago.

Slow Mover

Because of its size and weight, the Triceratops wouldn't have been able to move very quickly.

DID YOU KNOW?

Triceratops walked with its toes pointing outwards.

bony frill

Super Shields

The Triceratops had a bony frill to protect its neck and three horns that it would have used for fighting or to fend off attackers.

UP CLOSE

Which of these dinosaur close-ups shows part of a Triceratops?

a

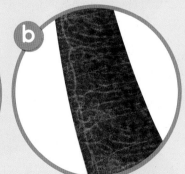

b

c

Answers on pages 76-77.

Dinosaur Doodles

It's drawing time! Follow the instructions to finish this prehistoric picture.

Draw lava erupting from the volcano.

Add some eggs to the dinosaur nest.

41

Deadly Giganotosaurus

This giant predator was one of the biggest dinosaurs.

DEADLY!

Deadliest Dino?

The gigantic Giganotosaurus was one of the deadliest of all the dinosaurs. Some estimates say it was bigger and heavier than the Tyrannosaurus.

DINO FACTS

NAME: Giganotosaurus
(gig-an-OH-toe-SORE-us)

MEANING:
Giant southern lizard

SIZE:

FOOD: Meat

Fossil Finds

Only one skeleton of a Giganotosaurus has ever been discovered. It was found in the desert in Argentina and is almost complete.

Sticking Together

It is thought that Giganotosaurus travelled in groups made up of dinosaurs of all ages, just like animals such as lions do today.

Brain Size

For such a huge dinosaur, Giganotosaurus actually had quite a small brain. It was about the size of a cucumber.

DINOSAUR DOODLE

Draw some sharp teeth inside this Giganotosaurus's mouth.

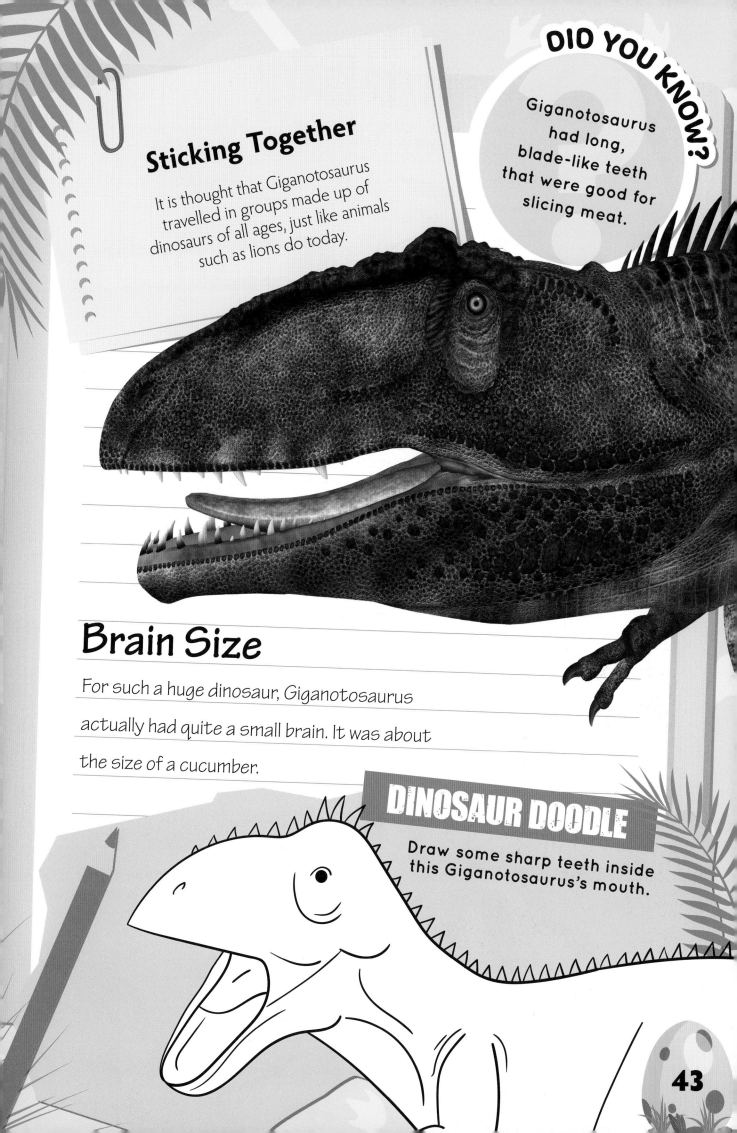

Dinosaur Dig

Have fun excavating your own dinosaur.

YOU WILL NEED

Small plastic box
(approx 9x9cm)

150g
cornflour

Bowl and
spoon

120ml water

Small plastic
dinosaur

Plastic
hammer

44

HOW TO MAKE

1

Weigh the cornflour and tip
it into a big bowl.

2

Measure the water and pour it on
top of the cornflour, a bit at a time,
mixing continuously.

3

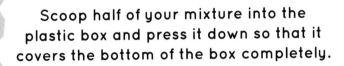

Scoop half of your mixture into the plastic box and press it down so that it covers the bottom of the box completely.

6

Carefully press your hardened mixture out of the box.

4

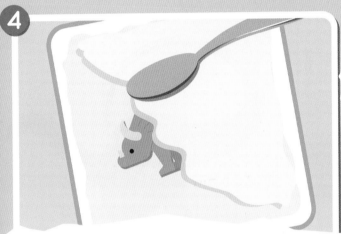

Press your plastic dinosaur into the mixture in the box then cover it with the remaining mixture so that it's completely hidden. Press the mixture into the corners of the box.

7

Use your tools to gently break the hardened mixture away to reveal the hidden dinosaur.

5

Put the box somewhere warm and, if possible, sunny. If any water pools on top of the mixture, carefully pour it away. Leave it for a day or so to completely harden until the surface begins to crack.

TOP TIP

If you want to make your excavation trickier, double, triple or quadruple the recipe and use a bigger box. You could also hide more than one dinosaur inside.

Tall Apatosaurus

Meet the big dinosaur with the noisy tail.

Noisy Tail

Apatosaurus had a long tail that helped it balance. It could also be cracked like a whip to make a sound louder than a cannon.

BOOM!

DINO FACTS

NAME: Apatosaurus
(ah-PAT-oh-sore-us)

MEANING:
Deceptive lizard

SIZE:

FOOD: Plants

Apatosaurus had spoon-shaped teeth.

Unusual Menu

Apatosaurus was a plant-eating dinosaur but it also swallowed stones! These helped grind up the food inside its massive stomach.

On the Move

It is thought that herds of Apatosaurus may have migrated, like many animals still do today.

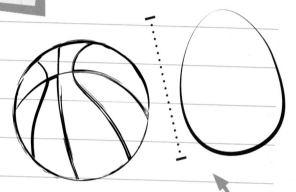

Big Eggs

Apatosaurus was a huge dinosaur that lived in the USA. It laid supersized eggs as big as basketballs.

PICK A PATH

Which path should the Apatosaurus take to reach its nest

a
b
c

Answers on pages 76-77.

Which Way?

START

This Velociraptor is in a hurry to get home. Can you guide it through the maze to its nest before the eggs hatch?

FINISH

Tick a circle as you spot each one.

Slow Stegosaurus

Introducing the big plate-backed dinosaur with the small brain.

DINO FACTS

NAME: Stegosaurus
(STEG-oh-SORE-us)

MEANING: Roof lizard

SIZE:

FOOD: Plants

Record Length

Stegosaurus lived in the USA 145 million years ago. It was as long as a bus making it the biggest of the plate-backed plant-eating dinosaurs.

Spiky Tail

Stegosaurus had a mighty tail which it could swing from side to side. The spike on the end made it a deadly weapon.

OUCH!

Slow Dino

When the first Stegosaurus fossils were found, scientists mistakenly thought that the dinosaur walked on two legs. It actually walked on four legs, very slowly.

Bony Back Plates

Scientists have suggested lots of uses for the Stegosaurus's back plates. They might have kept the dinosaur warm or cool, could have attracted mates or they may even have flashed red to warn off attackers.

STEGOSAURUS SHADOW

Which shadow belongs to the Stegosaurus?

a

b

Answers on pages 76-77.

It's Playtime!

The dinosaurs want to play! Carefully cut them out then stick them on to the scene.

Make sure you read page 54 before you cut out your dinosaurs. If you don't want to cut up your book, photocopy or scan and print this page instead..

Adult guidance is needed for this activity.

Heavy Iguanodon

Find out more about this bulky dinosaur
which had an unusual weapon.

DINO FACTS

NAME: Iguanodon
(ig-WHA-noh-don)

MEANING: Iguana tooth

SIZE:

FOOD: Plants

First Fossils

Almost 200 years ago miners in Sussex, England, found fossils of teeth. They belonged to an Iguanodon and it became the first ever dinosaur to be identified by a scientist.

Spiky Weapon

The Iguanodon had an unusual thumb spike on its hand which would have been used to fend off predators. A bit like having a built-in sword!

Easy Eating

Iguanodon had powerful jaws and curved teeth that were good for grinding food. These would have made it easier to eat the tough plants which grew at that time.

BULKY!

Heavy Load

Iguanodon was a heavy dinosaur. Its strong leg bones were designed to support its bulky body.

FAVE FOOD

Trace over the letters to write what Iguanodon liked to eat.

plants

Colour by Numbers

This Diplodocus needs some cool colours! Use the numbers and footprint key to help.

COUNT IT!

How many dinosaur fossils can you count on this page?

Answers on pages 76-77.

COLOUR KEY

1   2   3   4

Jumbled Up!

These dinosaurs have got themselves in a bit of a muddle! How many of each different dinosaur can you count?

Colour the dinosaur when you've finished.

Allosaurus   Spinosaurus   Velociraptor

Answers on pages 76-77.

57

Giant Brachiosaurus

This gigantic beast was taller than most houses!

DINO FACTS

NAME: Brachiosaurus
(BRAK-ee-oh-sore-us)

MEANING: Arm lizard

SIZE:

FOOD: Plants

LONG!

Heavy Load

Scientists have worked out that the supersized Brachiosaurus weighed as much as four African elephants. That's a whole lot of dinosaur!

Standing Tall

Brachiosaurus was a huge dinosaur with a really long neck. Its head reached as high as the fifth floor of a building. That's a long way up!

Green Diet

Brachiosaurus munched on leaves. It had long front legs and shorter back legs so it could easily reach tall tree-like plants.

Land Dino

Scientists used to think that Brachiosaurus lived in the water as it had nostrils on top of its head. But it is now believed to have been a land dinosaur.

FOOTPRINT PATTERN

What colour dinosaur footprint comes next in this sequence? Colour the last footprint the right colour.

Answers on pages 76-77.

Handprint Art

To make this awesome erupting volcano picture, all you'll need is some paint and your hands!

Make sure you read page 62 before you cut your volcano picture out. If you don't want to cut up your book, photocop or scan and print page 61 instead.

YOU WILL NEED

Red paint

Yellow paint

Paintbrush

Scissors

HOW TO MAKE

1. Ask an adult to cut out the picture of the volcano on the opposite page.

2. Use a paintbrush to cover one of your hands in yellow paint then make a handprint on the top of the volcano.

3. Wash your hand then cover it with red paint and make another handprint, overlapping the yellow one.

4. Leave to dry then hang your picture up for everyone to see.

! Adult guidance is needed for this activity.

Tiny Microraptor

This feathered dinosaur was small and speedy.

Tiny Dino

The mini Microraptor was one of the smallest meat-eating dinosaurs. It lived in China and was about the size of a seagull.

Fake Fossil

Scientists once thought they'd found a fossil which showed a link between birds and dinosaurs but it wasn't real. The fake fossil had been made by gluing the tail of a Microraptor to the front of an ancient bird!

Wing Power

Microraptors had feathered wings but they couldn't fly. Instead they used their wings to glide, perhaps by climbing trees and launching themselves into the air.

WHEEEEE!

Microraptor had a fan of feathers at the end of its tail which may have helped it balance in the air.

Tiny Predator

Meat-eating Microraptor had sharp claws and pointed teeth to help it catch and eat its prey. It dined on other animals and insects.

DINO FACTS

NAME: Microraptor
(MIKE-row-rap-tor)

MEANING: Small thief

SIZE:

FOOD: Meat

DINO DINNER

Draw some delicious insects for the meat-eating Microraptor.

Roar-some Race!

Will you be the first dinosaur to reach the cave in this exciting action game?

START

| | | 8  | 9 | 10 |

1

2

7

6

11

3   4    5

12

13

14

15

DINOSAUR KEY

FLAP LIKE A MICRORAPTOR AND MISS A GO.

STOMP LIKE A TRICERATOPS AND MOVE FORWARD 2 SPACES.

STRETCH LIKE A DIPLODOCUS AND MOVE BACK 1 SPACE.

ROAR LIKE A TYRANNOSAURUS AND ROLL AGAIN.

1. Carefully cut out the counters.

2. Take it in turns to roll the dice and move your counter around the board.

3. If you land on a dinosaur picture, follow the instructions in the Dinosaur Key.

4. The first player to reach the cave is the winner.

If you don't want to cut up your book, photocopy or scan and print page 65 instead.

Cut your counters out

20

21

22

23

19

24

18

25

17

26

16

FINISH

Adult guidance is needed for this activity.

Dinosaur Babies

Even the biggest predators started life in an egg.
Read on to find out more about young dinosaurs.

Warm Nest

Baby dinosaurs hatched from eggs. Just like birds do today, dinosaurs laid their eggs in nests. They probably covered them with leaves to keep them warm because if they'd sat on the eggs, they would have broken under their weight. Scrambled eggs anyone?

MISSING EGG

Can you spot this dinosaur egg hidden somewhere on these pages?

Dinosaur Eggs

The number of eggs laid was different for different kinds of dinosaur. Some laid more than 24 while others only laid a few. The eggs were often put in a spiral design inside the nest. That sounds egg-cellent!

Caring Parents

Some scientists believe that some baby dinosaurs couldn't walk when they were first hatched so their parents would have fed them in their nest. It's possible that the parents chewed up plants to feed their young.

Growing Up

Fossils have shown that young dinosaurs grew very quickly.

Meat-eaters would have learned to catch their prey by going on group hunts with adult dinosaurs.

Staying Safe

Many dinosaurs lived in herds. When they travelled as a group, plant-eaters would have kept their young in the middle of the group to protect them from predators.

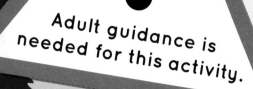

Dino Egg

Cute alert! Make your own hatching baby dinosaur with this egg-cellent craft!

Adult guidance is needed for this activity.

YOU WILL NEED

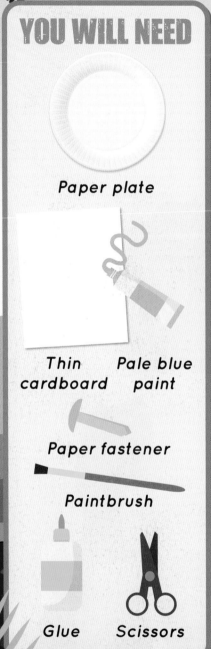

Paper plate

Thin cardboard

Pale blue paint

Paper fastener

Paintbrush

Glue

Scissors

HOW TO MAKE

1. Paint the paper plate pale blue and leave to dry completely.

2. Glue the baby dinosaur templates opposite on to thin card and carefully cut them out.

3. Once your paper plate is dry, cut it in half with a zig zag line

4. Use a paper fastener to attached the two halves of the plate together on the left-hand side.

5. Glue the baby dinosaur's head and tail onto the back of the bottom half of the plate, so that it looks like it's inside the egg.

6. Glue the dinosaur's feet onto the front of the bottom half of the plate so that the dinosaur looks like it's coming out of the egg.

7. Leave to dry then open and close your egg to hatch your very own cute baby dino!

68

Make sure you read page 70 before you cut out
the templates. If you don't want to cut up your book,
photocopy or scan and print this page instead.

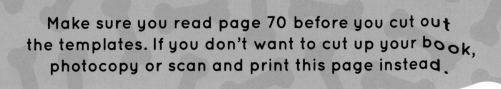

...e fish-eating Rhamphorhynchus
...ad teeth that slanted forwards and
interlocked. It was nocturnal which
means it slept in the daytime and
was awake at night.

...d...urs
only lived
on land.

Anhanguera (an-HAN-gwer-a)

...e Anhanguera had an impressive

...ngspan of 4.6m which is about the

...gth of a car. Imagine seeing that

...a through the sky towards you!

...s inner ear to help it balance

...head at an

PTERANODON TEASER

Look closely at these three Pteranodons.
Can you circle the biggest?

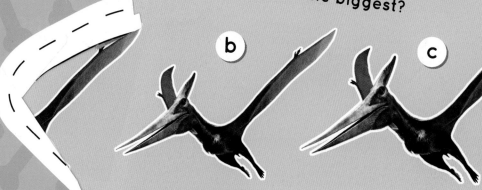

b

c

Prehistoric Sea Creatures

Find out about some of the marine reptiles that lived at the time of the dinosaurs.

Underwater Giants

In prehistoric times, marine reptiles could be found in oceans all over the world. The biggest ones are often mistaken for dinosaurs but true dinosaurs didn't live in the water.

Plesiosaurus
(PLE-see-oh-SORE-us)

Plesiosaurus had a broad body and short tail. It may have fed by swinging its long, snake-like neck from side to side through schools of fish and catching them with its sharp teeth.

Kronosaurus
(CRONE-oh-SORE-us)

Kronosaurus lived around 100 million years ago in the Australian seas. It was a supersized sea creature with four flippers, pointed teeth and a body as long as a bus.

Wow!

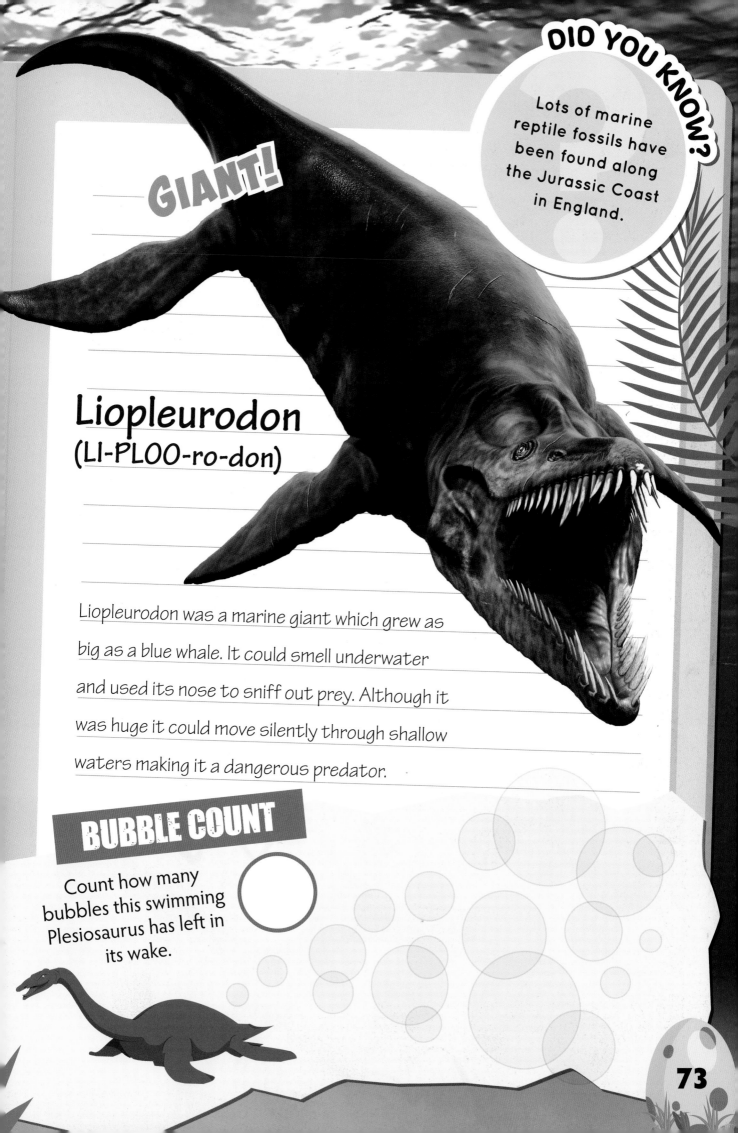

DID YOU KNOW?

Lots of marine reptile fossils have been found along the Jurassic Coast in England.

GIANT!

Liopleurodon
(LI-PLOO-ro-don)

Liopleurodon was a marine giant which grew as big as a blue whale. It could smell underwater and used its nose to sniff out prey. Although it was huge it could move silently through shallow waters making it a dangerous predator.

BUBBLE COUNT

Count how many bubbles this swimming Plesiosaurus has left in its wake.

Dino Quiz

? **?**

Do you know everything there is to know about dinosaurs? Find out by answering the questions below!

Tick true or false to answer each question. **?**

1. Tyrannosaurus ate meat.
TRUE ✓   FALSE

2. Diplodocus didn't have a tail.
TRUE   FALSE ✓

3. This is a Stegosaurus.
TRUE ✓   FALSE ✓

4. Pteranodon wasn't a dinosaur.
TRUE ✓   FALSE ✓

74

5. Triceratops had three horns.

TRUE   FALSE

6. Ankylosaurus was the fastest dinosaur.

TRUE   FALSE

7. Baby dinosaurs hatched from eggs.

TRUE   FALSE

8. Giganotosaurus was a small dinosaur.

TRUE   FALSE

HOW DID YOU DO?

1-2 correct: Uh oh, try again!
3-5 correct: Roar-some!
6-8 correct: Dino expert!

Answers

Pages 6-7 T.rex Teaser
Shadow a belongs to the Tyrannosaurus.

Pages 8-9 Prehistoric Search

Pages 10-11 Question Time
The Ankylosaurus liked to eat leaves.

Page 12 Dino Alert!
1- b, 2 – e, 3 – a, 4 – c, 5 – d.

Pages 14-15 Rhyme Time
Heat, feet and greet rhyme with meat.

Pages 18-19 Lots of Leaves
There are 15 leaves.

Pages 20-21 Heading Home
There are 3 fossils.

Pages 22-23 Fossil Fun
Fossil a shows the Diplodocus.

Pages 26-27 Quick Question
False – the Oviraptor didn't have any teeth.

Pages 28-29 Beat the Clock

Pages 30-31 Odd One Out
c.

Pages 32-33 Match It
1 – c, 2 – d, 3 – a, 4 – b.

There are 5 dinosaur eggs hidden on the pages.

Page 36 Who's Next?

Page 36 Count It!
There are 6 dinosaur footprints.

Pages 38-39 Up Close
c.

Pages 46-47 Pick a Path
c.

Pages 48-49 Which Way?

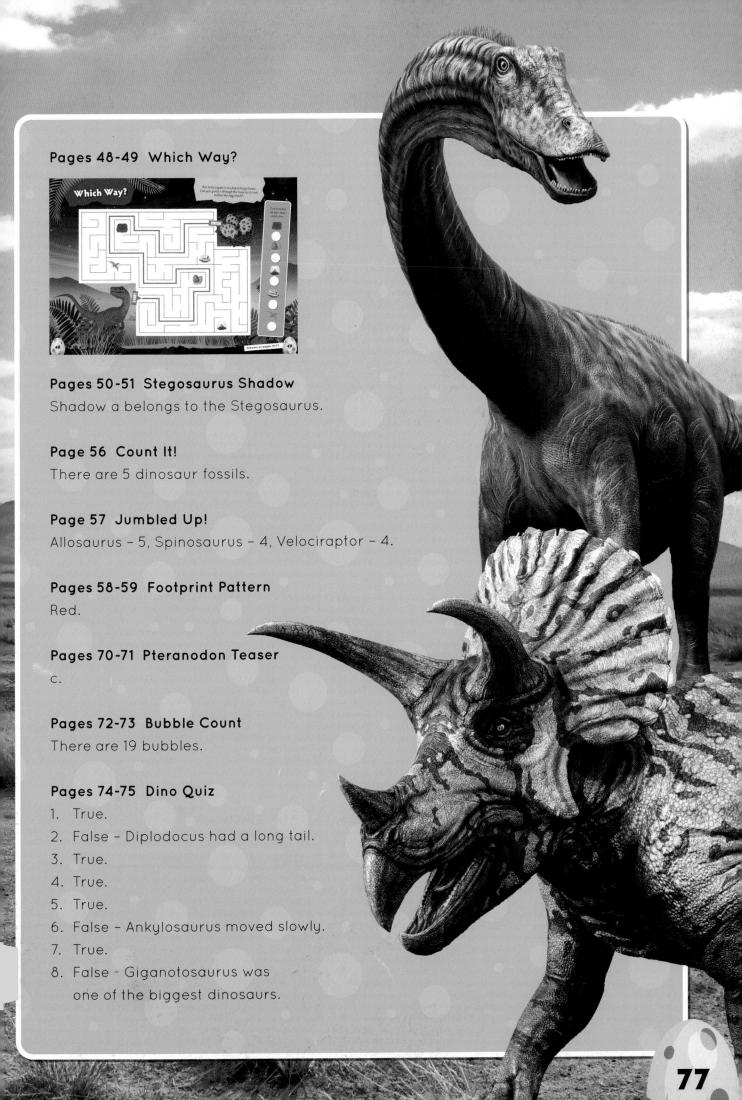

Pages 50-51 Stegosaurus Shadow

Shadow a belongs to the Stegosaurus.

Page 56 Count It!

There are 5 dinosaur fossils.

Page 57 Jumbled Up!

Allosaurus – 5, Spinosaurus – 4, Velociraptor – 4.

Pages 58-59 Footprint Pattern

Red.

Pages 70-71 Pteranodon Teaser

c.

Pages 72-73 Bubble Count

There are 19 bubbles.

Pages 74-75 Dino Quiz

1. True.
2. False – Diplodocus had a long tail.
3. True.
4. True.
5. True.
6. False – Ankylosaurus moved slowly.
7. True.
8. False - Giganotosaurus was
    one of the biggest dinosaurs.